HALF-TIME PIES

HALF-TIME CAKES

MORE HALF-TIME PIES

BULLYING FOR DUMMIES

BANG!

ANSWER:
LEFT TO RIGHT: DIRTY DICK, THE JOCKS, CUDDLES, DESPERATE DAN, GREEDY PIGG, SMASHER, BULLY BEEF, CORPORAL CLOTT.

THIS BOOK BELONGS TO:

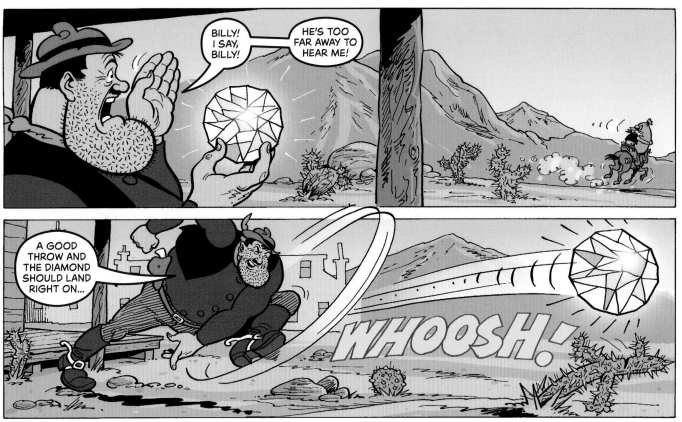

WANTED

How much reward money do you stand to get for rounding up all the outlaws?

PAW CLANTON	REWARD $100	CURLY PHIL	REWARD $300
MAD DOG MADDEN	REWARD $500	CURTIS SNAKE	REWARD $300
BUTCH CASSIDY	REWARD $1000	JED DRUMSTICK	REWARD $500
SUNDANCE KID	REWARD $1000	BULLSEYE BILL	REWARD $200
JESSE JAMES	REWARD $500	SLY KEV	REWARD $600

REWARD MONEY COLLECTED:

D	J	E	S	S	E	J	A	M	E	S	M	J
I	R	G	N	F	G	V	E	H	E	A	E	B
K	U	K	Q	J	Q	R	N	Q	D	D	L	U
E	L	V	M	W	P	X	A	D	D	D	I	L
C	M	R	S	F	U	D	O	R	L	E	H	L
N	X	H	W	N	J	G	U	J	E	D	P	S
A	C	A	G	B	M	M	C	Y	U	T	Y	E
D	G	T	V	A	S	L	Y	K	E	V	L	Y
N	R	T	D	T	Y	O	S	Y	I	J	R	E
U	Y	D	I	S	S	A	C	H	C	T	U	B
S	E	C	L	R	Z	B	O	G	E	B	C	I
N	K	P	A	W	C	L	A	N	T	O	N	L
E	K	A	N	S	S	I	T	R	U	C	L	L

CACTUSVILLE JAIL

SOLUTION: You'd earn $5,000!

KHH.

THE DANDYTOWN WORLD CUP!

PART ONE

IT'S TIME FOR THE DANDYTOWN WORLD CUP FINAL!

WHO COULD FORGET WHAT HAPPENED IN THE LAST ONE?

ME, ACTUALLY!

I HAVE NO IDEA WHAT HAPPENED!

I PROMISE TO PAY MORE ATTENTION THIS TIME!

DANDYTOWN STADIUM

THE TEAMS ARE THE SAME AS THE LAST FINAL, APPARENTLY! FOR DANDYTOWN UNITED, IT'S DESPERATE DAN, CORPORAL CLOTT, GREEDY PIGG, SMASHER, BULLY BEEF, DIRTY DICK, CUDDLES, AND THE JOCKS...

...AND FOR DANDYTOWN ROVERS IT'S BRASSNECK, BLINKY, WINKER WATSON, THE GEORDIES, KEYHOLE KATE, DIMPLES, BERYL THE PERIL, BAD GRANDAD, AND CHIPS!

NIGEL PARKINSON.

YOU'RE LOVELY, AREN'T YOU! YES, YOU ARE! YOU'RE LOVELY!

YOU BEAUTIFUL, BEAUTIFUL THING!

MY WONDERFUL NEW CAR!

IT DOESN'T LOOK NEW, YOUR LORDSHIP!

IT LOOKS THE OPPOSITE OF NEW.

IT'S NEW TO ME!

THIS IS AN ORIGINAL AUSTIN EIGHT STAFF CAR, MADE AT THE START OF WORLD WAR TWO! IT'S A CLASSIC!

COULD YOU NOT AFFORD A NEW CAR, YOUR LORDSHIP?

THIS IS BETTER THAN A HORRIBLE NEW CAR, AND STOP CALLING ME 'YOUR LORDSHIP'! IT'S 'COLONEL' OR 'SIR'!

AYE, AYE, CAPTAIN!

JUST GET AWAY FROM IT! SHOO! SHOO! GO PAINT THE GUARD TOWER!

SHOVE

SO CLOTT PAINTS THE GUARD TOWER...

VERY NICE, CLOTT...

...BUT THIS IS THE ARMY, NOT ART COLLEGE!

PUT THIS PAINT!

ON THAT!

GET IT?

YES, YOUR MAJESTY!

CLOTT CARRIES THE FIRST POT UP...

PHEW!

BRASSNECK'S CHALLENGED ME TO SOME WINTER GAMES!

FIRST UP - BUILDING A SNOWMAN!

FINISHED. BEAT THAT, BRASSNECK!

IT'S A SNOW-ROBOT. ONE-NIL TO ME!

CLONK!

NEXT - SNOWBALL FIGHT...

AMMO

SPLAT!

...AND I'M A DEAD SHOT. TAKE THAT!

OO-ER!

WHIRRRR...

TWO-NIL.

BLAM! BLAM! BLAM! BLAM! BLAM!

WAH!

SPLATTER!

KEYHOLE KATE

Kate (off-panel): THOSE CAKES LOOK DELICIOUS, MUM! CAN YOU PUSH ONE THROUGH THE KEYHOLE TO ME?

Mum: EEK! WHAT?

Mum: KATE! PEEPING THROUGH THE KEYHOLE AGAIN! I SHOULD HAVE KNOWN!

Kate: OOPS!

Bert: KATE JUST NEEDS A FRIEND TO TAKE HER MIND OFF KEYHOLES! I MAY HAVE A SOLUTION AT LAST!

KATE'S MAD INVENTOR UNCLE, BLACK HOLE BERT.

Kate: ANOTHER ONE OF YOUR MAD INVENTIONS, BERT?

Bert: KATE, MEET DUPLI-KATE, YOUR ROBOT TWIN!

Dupli-Kate: BZZT! HI, KATE! LET'S PLAY!

Kate: SO COOL! THANKS, UNCLE!

Bert: I'VE PROGRAMMED DUPLI-KATE TO HAVE ALL THE SAME INTERESTS AS KATE, EXCEPT FOR KEYHOLE SNOOPING!

Bert: BRILLIANT! SHE'LL SOON FORGET ABOUT KEYHOLES NOW!

LATER...

Kate: HEY, DUPLI-KATE. IF YOU'RE PROGRAMMED TO BE MY ROBOT TWIN, YOU CAN DO MY HOMEWORK!

Dupli-Kate: BZZT! HAPPY TO HELP TO THE BEST OF MY ABILITY!

Kate: RESULT! NOW I CAN BUNK OFF AND GO SNOOPING!

Kate: BRILLIANT! HAVING DUPLI-KATE DO MY HOMEWORK FROM NOW ON GIVES ME EVEN MORE TIME TO LOOK THROUGH KEYHOLES!

13

NEXT DAY...

GRAB!

Dupli-Kate: HEE-HEE! HAVING A COMPUTER BRAIN DO MY HOMEWORK WILL PUT ME TOP OF THE CLASS!

AT SCHOOL...

Teacher: KATE! WHAT'S THE MEANING OF THIS SILLINESS? FOR THAT I'LL GIVE YOU DOUBLE HOMEWORK TONIGHT!

1: I DON'T KNOW! 2: NOT A CLUE! 3: DUNNO!
A: YOU TELL ME!
4: WHO KNOWS?
5: NO IDEA!
I DON'T KNOW

Kate: ARGH! IT WAS A DOUBLE THAT GOT ME INTO THIS MESS! MY ROBOT ISN'T VERY SMART!

KATE or DUPLI-KATE?

KEYHOLE KATE'S MAD INVENTOR UNCLE, BLACK HOLE BERT, HAS CREATED EVEN MORE ROBOT DUPLI-KATES! THEY'RE NOT ALL PERFECT THOUGH! THE REAL KATE HAS HIDDEN HERSELF AMONGST THEM. CAN YOU SPOT HER?

CLUES:
THE REAL KATE HAS:
- TWO PIGTAILS
- GLASSES
- SHORT SLEEVES
- RED DRESS
- NO HAT
- SLIP-ON SHOES
- YELLOW BOWS IN HER PIGTAILS
- BLACK TIGHTS

ANSWER: K

CUDDLES and DIMPLES

WE, ER... HAVE A REQUISITION FROM THE HEAD! WE NEED ALL THE LIGHTS - CHRISTMAS LIGHTS, FLOODLIGHTS FROM THE CRICKET PITCH...

WHY IS THIS WRITTEN ON A CRISP PACKET?

BECAUSE IT'S FOR A VERY IMPORTANT WELCOME SHOW FOR A VISITING DIGNITARY. LOOK... THE ROYAL SEAL OF THE KINGDOM OF... QUA-VERS!

THIS LOOKS LIKE A JAM STAIN!

LOOK, LADS, I'M SURE WHATEVER YOU'RE UP TO IS A LOT OF FUN, BUT...

I'LL GIVE YOU MY SKYFLIX LOGIN!

DEAL! JUST DON'T BREAK ANYTHING.

WE WON'T!

WARDROBE AND EFFECTS DONE. WHAT'S NEXT?

MAKE-UP! FOLLOW ME!

WINKER'S MOVIE
PRODUCTION SCHEDULE
- WARDROBE
- EFFECTS
- MAKE-UP

TO THE AQUARIUM?

CALM WATERS, OLD CHUM, IS THE COAST CLEAR YET?

I HOPE YOU KNOW WHAT YOU'RE DOING, THIS IS TOO FISHY FOR ME.

I'LL BRING IT BACK SAFELY, DON'T WORRY!

EVERYTHING READY?

THE HEAD IS IN HIS STUDY HAVING HIS DAILY NAP...

...AND CREEPY IS JUST ABOUT TO RELAX WITH HIS FAVOURITE RADIO SHOW!

PERFECT!

ACTION!

LADIES AND GENTLEMEN, DO NOT PANIC. WE INTERRUPT THIS BROADCAST TO BRING YOU URGENT NEWS!

PLANET EARTH, OUR HOME, HAS BEEN INVADED BY STRANGE BEINGS IN FLYING SAUCERS...

MARTIANS! MOONMEN! THEY WOULDN'T COME HERE, WOULD THEY?

HIT THE LIGHTS, TIMMY!

ROGER, WINKER!

FZZZT!

THE INVADERS WERE LAST SEEN OVER GREYTOWERS SCHOOL IN DANDYTOWN...

ARRGH! THEY'RE HERE! HELP!

I'D BETTER WARN THE HEAD!

HE'S ON THE WAY TO THE HEAD'S OFFICE. YOU KNOW WHAT TO DO!

IN THE HEAD'S OFFICE...

ROGER THAT, WINKER.

BRAAAP!

DONK!

ARRGH! AIR RAID! GET TO COVER! SAVE YOURSELVES!

GLUB!

SPLOP!

MFFFRRELL!

KRISH!

HEAD! THE ALIENS ARE HERE! THE ALIENS ARE...

...ARRGH! AN ALIEN!

SLAM!

MFFFRRELL!

SPARE ME, MIGHTY INVADERS, TAKE THE BOYS INSTEAD!

CREEP? WHAT ARE YOU DOING? IS IT DINNER TIME? YOU KNOW I DON'T LIKE SEAFOOD!

CUT! THAT'S A WRAP!

GET BACK HERE! I'LL LAUNCH THE LOT OF YOU INTO SPACE WHEN I CATCH YOU!

I DON'T THINK THE MOVIE BUSINESS IS FOR YOU, SIR! DON'T GIVE UP YOUR DAY JOB!

THE BOYS ESCAPE...

THAT WAS GREAT! PUT THE VIDEO ON GREYTOWERS' YOUTUBE CHANNEL. WE MIGHT GET SOME EXTRA MARKS FOR DRAMA CLASS!

THE NEXT MORNING...

THAT WAS A GOOD BIT OF FUN YESTERDAY, EH?

IT CERTAINLY MADE UP FOR MISSING THE MOVIE.

PITY WE DIDN'T GET TO SEE THE FILM, THOUGH.

IS THERE... A FROG IN MY PORRIDGE?

LADS, HAVE YOU SEEN THE VIEWS ON OUR YOUTUBE VIDEO? WE'VE GONE VIRAL! OUR SPACE FILM IS A HIT!

DING DONG!

WHO'S THIS, THEN?

HOPEFULLY IT'S THE POLICE HERE TO ARREST YOU FOR KIDNAPPING THAT POOR OCTOPUS.

THE CAST OF SPACE WARS?!

WE LOVED YOUR VIDEO SO MUCH WE HAD TO COME AND MEET ITS STARS!

OUTTA THIS WORLD!

WOW! TROTTY IS REALLY REAL!

KORKY THE CAT

DESPERATE DAN!

DINAH MO

Winker WATSON

WHERE'S WINKER? HE'S NORMALLY FIRST IN LINE FOR A SCHOOL TRIP.

SORRY I'M LATE, LADS. I JUST NEEDED A FEW LAST MINUTE BITS AND PIECES.

WOW! YOU'RE WELL PREPARED.

OF COURSE! A WEEKEND IN THE COUNTRYSIDE...

...FISHING, CLIMBING, FRESH AIR, SUNSHINE...

WATSON! WHAT ARE YOU DOING WITH ALL THIS JUNK? WE'RE GOING *CAMPING*, NOT ON HOLIDAY!

POF!

GET RID OF IT!

THIS TRIP IS ABOUT BUILDING CHARACTER AND LEARNING VALUABLE LIFE SKILLS, NOT IDLE WHIMSY!

SEVERAL HOURS OF BUMPY BUS JOURNEY LATER...

HERE WE ARE! HOME FOR THE NEXT FEW DAYS.

THIS IS *NOT* WHAT I IMAGINED.

ARE THOSE VULTURES?

WELCOME TO ~~SCENIC~~ BLEAK PEAK

NO, MR TROTT, THOSE ARE NOT VULTURES. THOSE ARE, ERM... TUFTED HIGHLAND WUMBLERS.

TIME TO SET UP CAMP!

ARE THE TENTS ON THE BUS?

NO TENTS, WATSON! BOYS YOUR AGE MUST LEARN *SURVIVAL* SKILLS.

THIS WEEKEND YOU WILL BE BUILDING YOUR OWN SHELTERS AND FORAGING FOR YOUR OWN FOOD!

WHAT?! BUILDING? FORAGING? WHAT ABOUT YOU TWO?

DON'T WORRY ABOUT US, WATSON.

WE'VE ALL THE SKILLS AND CHARACTER WE NEED ALREADY!

THE BOYS SET OFF TO FIND MATERIALS FOR A SHELTER...

I DON'T NEED TO BUILD CHARACTER - I'VE GOT LOADS!

AND WHY DO WE NEED SURVIVAL SKILLS WHEN WE HAVE SMARTPHONES?

THERE'S BOUND TO BE AN APP FOR THIS!

THE BOYS TRY TO FORAGE SOME LUNCH...

BACK AT CAMP...

NONSENSE, CREEP! WE'RE THE FIRST PEOPLE TO SEE THIS BIRD IN OVER A HUNDRED YEARS! WE OWE IT TO *SCIENCE!*

GROAN!

SPLORTCH!

SPLUTCH!

TEN MINUTES LATER...

ANY IDEA WHERE IT WENT?

DING!

HANG ON, I'VE GOT A MESSAGE.

THAT WASN'T A FLIGHTLESS WANGLETHRIP, SIR! IT APPEARS IT WAS JUST A *WANGLE.*

70%

WATSON: Building character, Sir?

WINKER! GRRR! JUST YOU WAIT TILL I GET BACK TO CAMP!

THIS IS MORE LIKE IT! WE'VE ALL THE LIFE SKILLS WE NEED ALREADY.

HERE'S THE WILDLIFE TRUST, WINKER, WHAT WILL WE TELL THEM?

WILDLIFE TRUST

RAAAGH! WINKER!

GRRR!

THESE MUST BE THE *RARE SPECIES* YOU PHONED US ABOUT!

GASP! LESSER-SPOTTED HIGHLAND BOG-YETIS! TWO OF 'EM!

ARGLE-BARGLE!

DON'T WORRY, LADS, WE'LL TAKE THEM AND RELEASE THEM INTO THE REMOTE MARSHES THEY CAME FROM.

WHERE ARE YOUR TEACHERS?

NNNGH! GRRR!

I THINK THE YETIS GOT THEM.

DON'T WORRY, GUYS. WE'LL GET YOU LOOKED AFTER UNTIL YOU CAN BE BROUGHT HOME.

WI...

A SCHOOL GROUP WAS TERRORISED BY HIGHLAND BOG-YETIS ON BLEAK PEAK TODAY. THIRTY SCHOOLBOYS WERE RESCUED, BUT AUTHORITIES ARE STILL SEARCHING FOR TWO TEACHERS WHOM IT IS FEARED MAY HAVE BEEN EATEN...

NEWS

HOTEL Le Fancy ★★★★★

OH, *A LITTLE BIRDIE* TELLS ME THEY'LL SURVIVE SOMEHOW!

HOTEL Le Fancy

AR!

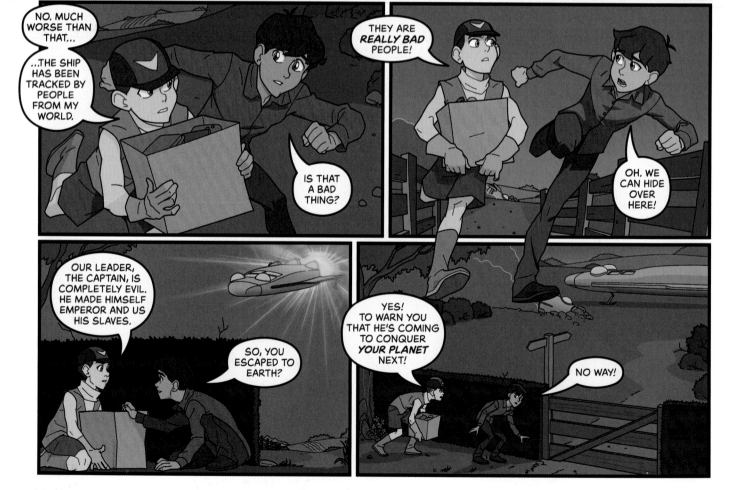

DIRECT HIT. WE GOT IT!

SLIP!

THUNK!

OUCH! THAT'S GOT TO HURT.

IT'S KNOCKED OUT COLD!

I'VE NEVER SEEN ANYTHING LIKE IT IN ALL MY DAYS.

WE CAN USE IT AS MORE PROOF THAT AN INVASION IS COMING!

ZZZZ!

SO...

DOES YOUR WORLD HAVE A PRESIDENT OR A KING?

WE HAVE LOTS. WE'RE NOT JUST ONE COUNTRY HERE.

LOOK - THERE'S A POLICE OFFICER.

JACK TRIES TO EXPLAIN...

IS THIS SOME KIND OF JOKE?

WHY WOULD I JOKE ABOUT THIS?

THE ARMY ARE CALLED...

WHY SHOULD WE TRUST YOU? YOU BROUGHT THIS MONSTER WITH YOU.

IT CAME AFTER ME TO CATCH ME AND TAKE ME BACK.

HE CAME HERE TO WARN US.

ZZZZ!

WARN US OF AN ALIEN INVASION? WHAT ABSOLUTE NONSENSE. THIS IS SOME KIND OF SCHOOLBOY TRICK.

WHAT ABOUT THAT? IS THAT A TRICK?

CORPORAL CLOTT

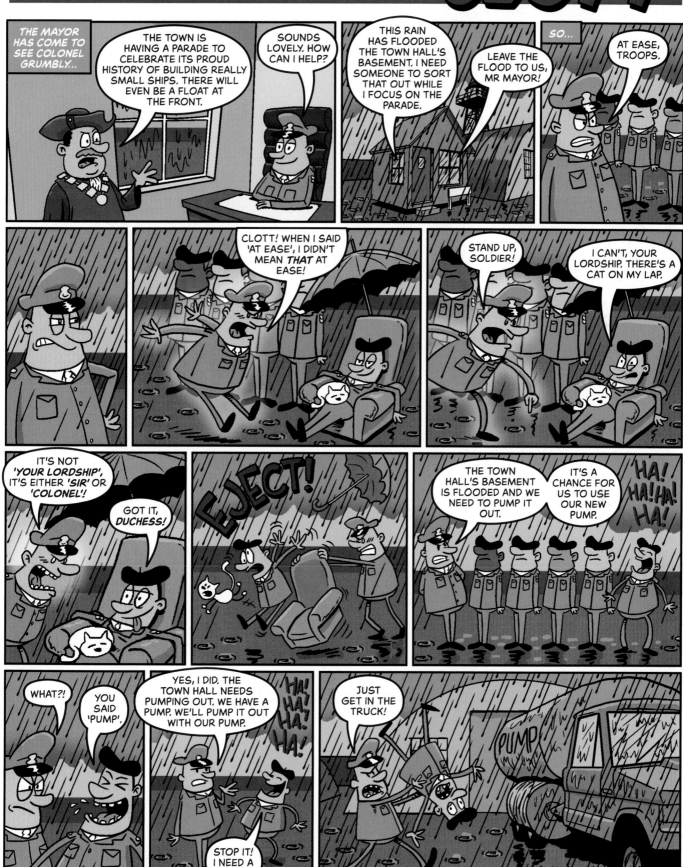

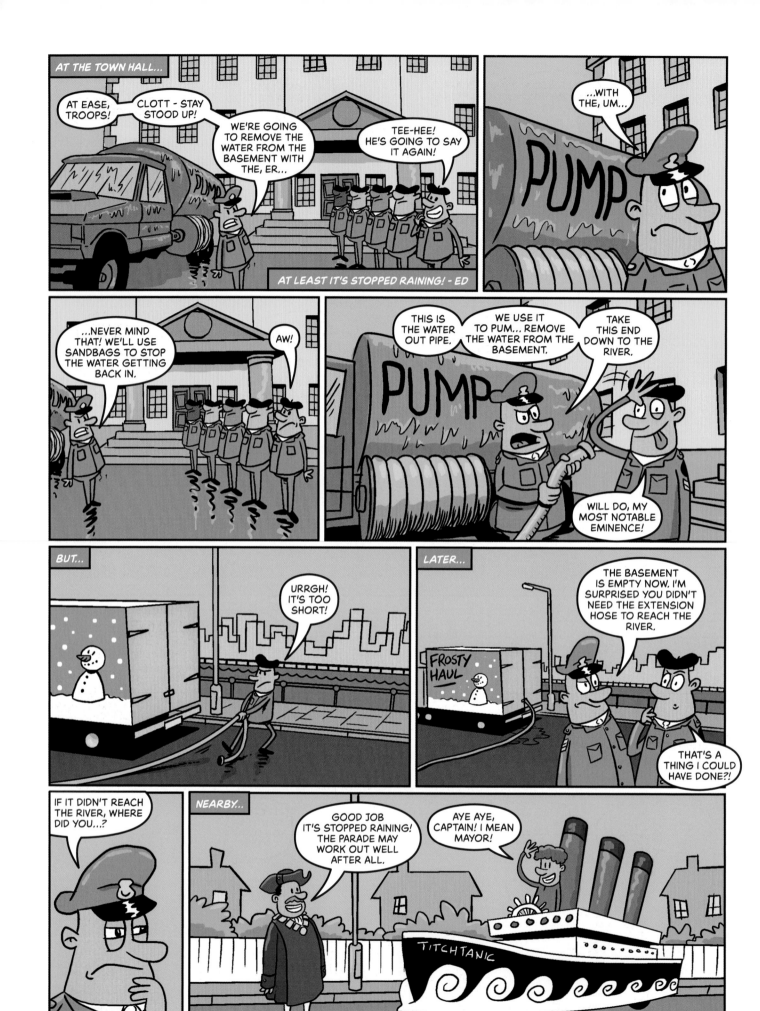

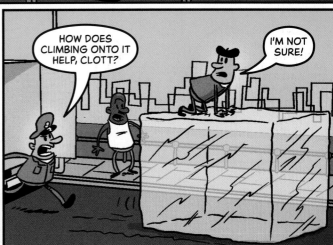

KEYHOLE KATE

DINAH MO

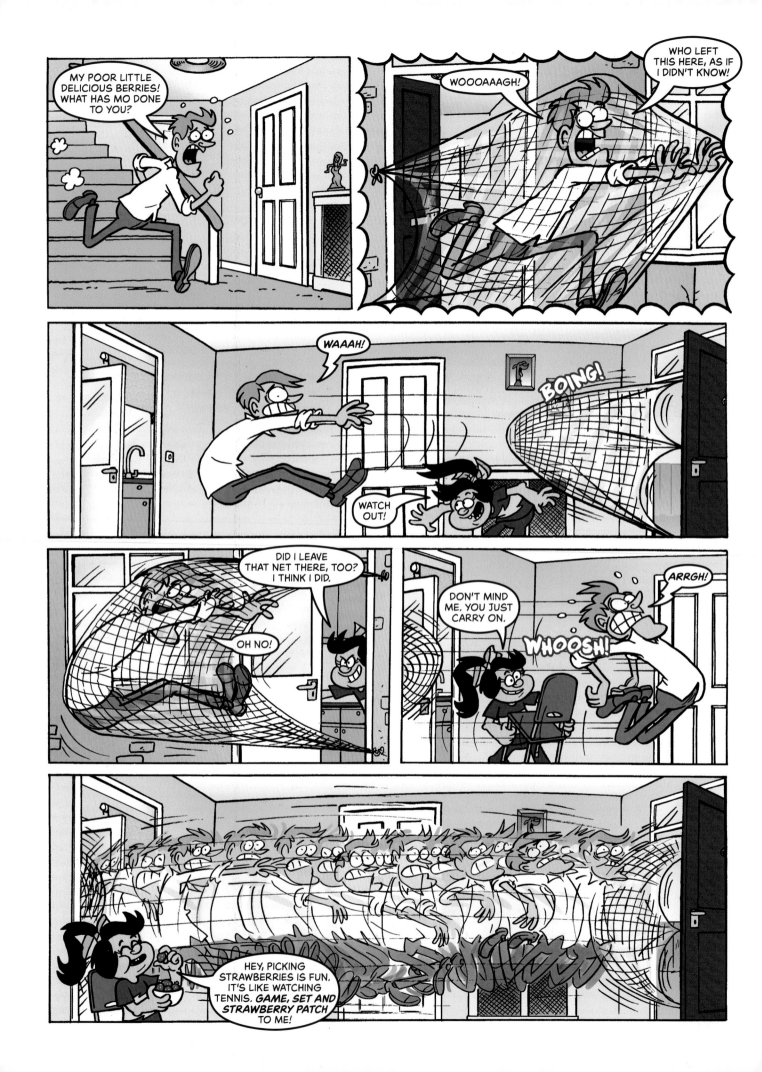

KORKY THE CAT

FIVE MINUTES LATER...

GUTEN TAG! I AM OF COURSE BRIAN MUNICH, MOST FAMOUS GOALKEEPER OF GERMANY, JA?

BRIAN MUNICH IS OVER SIX FEET TALL. GO AWAY!

OWEN TRIES HIS LAST DISGUISE...

EVENING, ME OLD CHINA! I'M...

RONNY CASH, THE FAMOUS FOOTBALL AGENT! WELCOME, MR CASH, ENJOY THE SHOW!

I'M IN! I CAN'T BELIEVE IT! NOW TO FIND SCRUFFI.

IMPOSTER!

YIKES! THE ACTUAL RONNY CASH!

SECURITY! GET THIS PHONY FACSIMILE OUT OF HERE!

AND DON'T COME BACK!

WAH!

HOOF

OWEN GOES TO THE PARK FOR A KICKABOUT...

SIGH. ALL I WANTED WAS TO SAY HELLO TO SCRUFFI AND MAYBE GET A FOOTY TIP OR TWO.

HEY, AMIGO, PASS THE BALL!

I OVERHEARD YOU. I'M GOING TO THE GALA. IF I MEET THIS SCRUFFI, I'LL TELL HIM YOU SAY HI!

THANKS, BUT I'M SURE A BIG CELEB LIKE HIM WON'T CARE.

OH, I DON'T KNOW... MAYBE CONSTANTINO SCRUFFI DOESN'T CARE FOR CELEBRITY.

MAYBE HE IS HAPPIER TO BE OUT HERE IN A SUNNY PARK HAVING A KICKABOUT.

HERE, TRY THIS NEXT TIME YOU PASS - STAND LIKE THIS, AND STRIKE WITH THIS PART OF THE FOOT.

WOW! THANKS, I WILL!

IF YOU SEE HIM, MY NAME IS OWEN GOAL! HEY, I DIDN'T CATCH YOURS!

SPLENDIFICO!

WHAT A NICE MAN, I HOPE HE GETS TO MEET...

...SCRUFFI!

HA-HA! BETTER LUCK NEXT TIME, OWEN! - ED

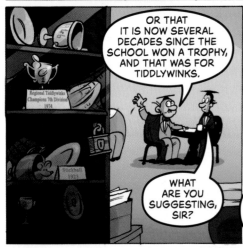

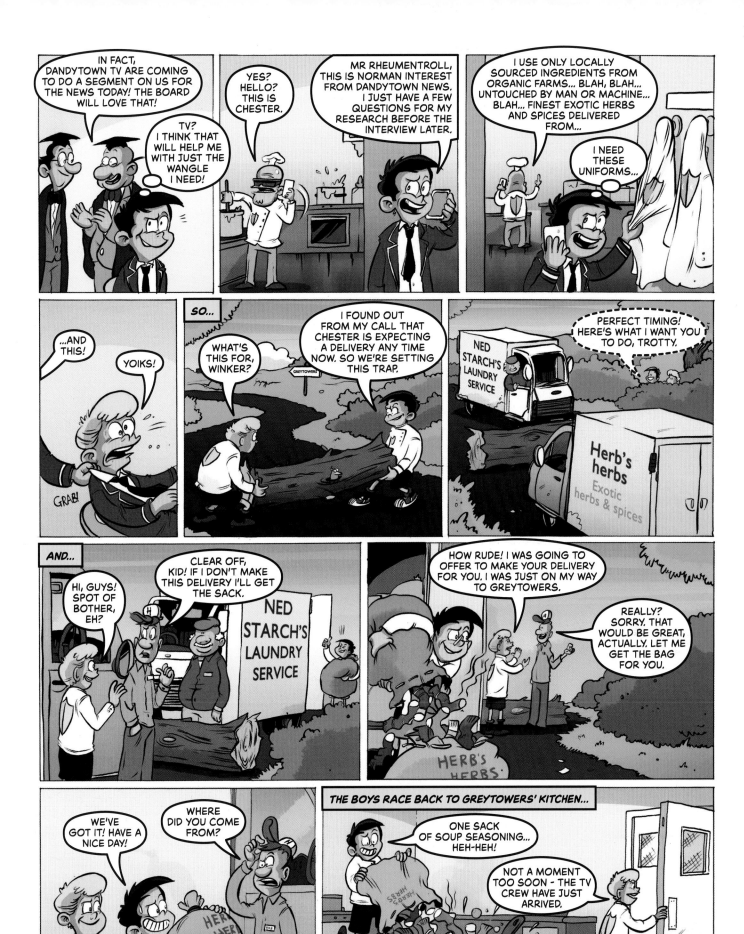

DESPERATE DAN!

THE DANDYTOWN WORLD CUP! PART THREE

SECOND HALF

PART THREE IS THE SECOND HALF?! THAT DOESN'T MAKE SENSE! - ED

WELCOME BACK TO THE SECOND HALF OF THE DANDYTOWN WORLD CUP FINAL. THE SCORE STANDS AT ONE-ALL, SO THERE'S STILL EVERYTHING TO PLAY FOR...

SUPPORT

I'M HERE BY MISTAKE

I ♥ FOOTBALL

ROAR!

MY TEAM

YAY!

GO!

US!

THE PEOPLE BEHIND ME CAN'T SEE!!

MEANWHILE, IN PARIS...

ARE YOU OKAY, MY LOVE? THAT BALL DID HIT YOU PRETTY HARD, AND THE WATER IS VERY COLD.

WH-WH-WHAT WERE YOU ASKING M-M-ME BEFORE I WAS KNOCKED OUT OF THE B-B-BOAT?

BACK IN DANDYTOWN...

I'VE GOT THE BALL!

IT'S STILL ROMANTIC. WE'RE STILL IN PARIS...

...I'LL STILL ASK HER TO MARRY ME.

DESPERATE DAN TAKES POSSESSION OF THE BALL...

BOOT!

DANDYTOWN STADIUM

DARLING, WILL YOU...

BISH!

SPLASH!

...NEVER MIND, IT'S NOT IMPORTANT!

BRASSNECK TAKES THE THROW IN FOR DANDYTOWN ROVERS...

# KEYHOLE KATE

DINAH MO

HI, GRAN. READY TO SKATEBOARD DOWN TO THE FOOTBALL MATCH AND SOAK THE OPPOSITION?

I'M FEELING POORLY, MO.

BUT THE SKATEBOARD AND THE FOOTY AND THE SOAKER...

LISTEN UP, KIDDO. I'M ON TO A GOOD THING HERE.

OH, IT'S A SCAM. THAT'S ALL RIGHT, THEN.

THIS WILL HELP YOU GET UP THE STAIRS, DEARIE.

'DEARIE', DID HE SAY?

HE CALLED GRAN 'DEARIE', HE'S DOOMED.

COULD YOU DEMONSTRATE IT?

SURE THING.

WHAT DOES THIS DO?

DON'T PRESS THAT! IT'S...

...ARRGH!

AWESOME? I AGREE!

I CAN'T WAIT TO GIVE IT A GO.

MUMMY!

WHAT A SHOT, RIGHT THROUGH THE WINDOW.

JUST AS WELL I LEFT IT OPEN!

ARE YOU THINKING WHAT I'M THINKING, GRAN?

DEPENDS. ARE YOU THINKING ABOUT CHOCOLATE HOBNOBS?

TURN OVER TO SEE WHAT DINAH MO AND GRAN BUILT!

KORKY THE CAT

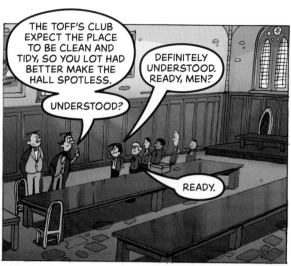

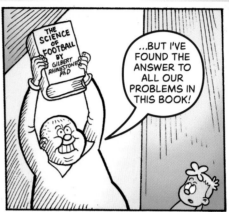

CORPORAL CLOTT

WHAT DO YOU WANT, DOCTOR ODDBODS?

I WANT ONE OF YOUR SOLDIERS FOR MY EXPERIMENT!

I'LL NEED TO TAKE AWAY ONE OF YOUR MEN FOR A WEEK.

I KNOW JUST THE MAN!

SO...

LISTEN UP, CLOTT! SOMETIMES REAL, ACTUAL SOLDIERS ARE POSTED IN REMOTE, FAR AWAY PLACES.

IT'S IMPORTANT TO KNOW THE EFFECTS OF BOREDOM ON THE HUMAN MIND...

...SO DOCTOR ODDBODS IS GOING TO LOCK YOU IN THIS CHAMBER FOR A WEEK WITH NOTHING TO DO TO SEE HOW THAT AFFECTS YOU.

SIR! YES, SIR!

OKAY, ODDBOD, YOU CAN LET ME OUT NOW!

WHAT ARE YOU DOING IN THERE? THE EXPERIMENT HAS BEGUN!

WELL UNBEGIN IT AND LET ME OUT!

I CAN'T! IT'S ON A TIME LOCK!

OF COURSE IT IS!

YAY! A WEEK WITH MY BEST BUDDY, MR GRUMBLY!

LATER...

I SPY WITH MY LITTLE EYE, SOMETHING BEGINNING WITH... 'D'!

DOOR! FOR THE TENTH TIME! IT'S DOOR! EVERY TIME YOU LOOK AROUND THE CHAMBER YOU LOOK AT THE DOOR THEN SAY, 'SOMETHING BEGINNING WITH 'D'!'

BUT THE ONLY THING IN HERE IS A DOOR, APART FROM THE SEATS. OH! I JUST THOUGHT OF ONE! SOMETHING BEGINNING WITH 'S'!

ARRGH!

LET'S TRY ANOTHER GAME. I WENT TO THE SHOPS AND I BOUGHT... POTATOES.

BUT HOW? THE DOOR'S LOCKED.

NO! IT'S A MEMORY GAME. YOU HAVE TO REMEMBER EVERYTHING ON THE LIST THEN ADD YOUR OWN THING.

DESPERATE DAN!

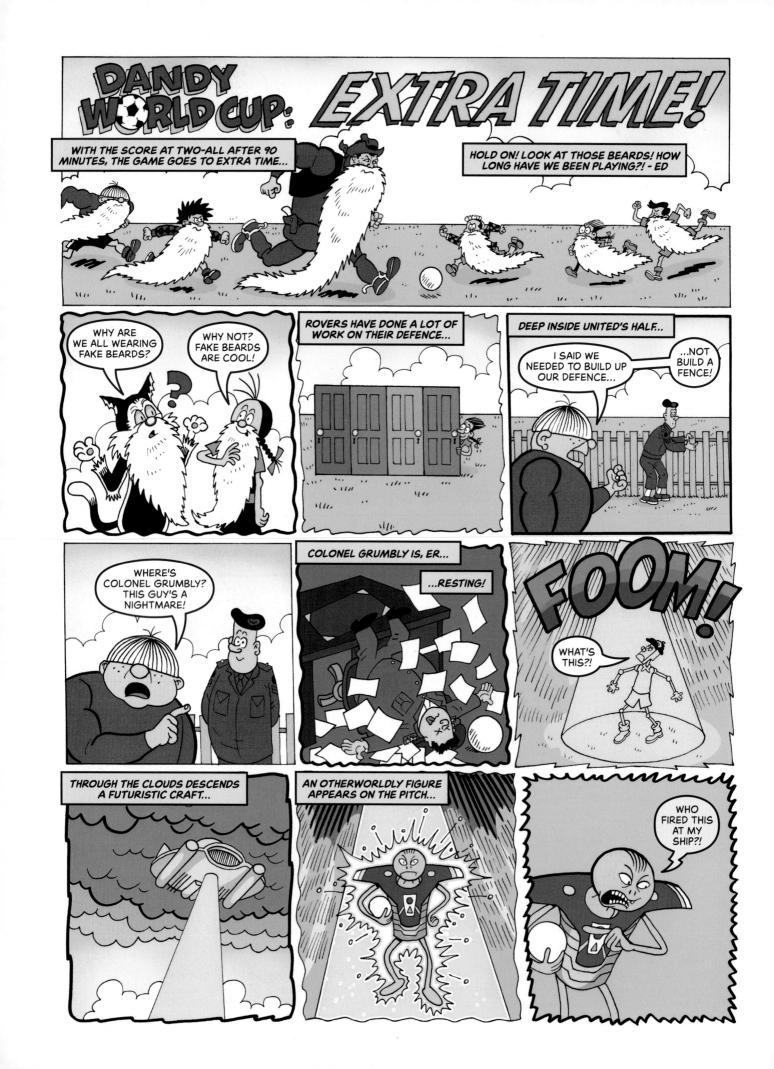